Return of the Jets

Janice Pimm • Jon Stuart

Contents

OXFORD
UNIVERSITY PRESS

Macro Marvel
(billionaire inventor)

Welcome to Micro World!

Macro Marvel invented Micro World – a micro-sized theme park where you have to shrink to get in.

A computer called **CODE** controls Micro World and all the robots inside – MITEs and BITEs.

A MITE

A BITE

Disaster strikes!

CODE goes wrong on opening day.
CODE wants to shrink the world.

Macro Marvel is trapped inside the park ...

Enter Team X!

Four micro agents – *Max, Cat, Ant* and *Tiger* – are sent to rescue Macro Marvel and defeat CODE.

Mini Marvel joins Team X.

Mini Marvel
(Macro's daughter)

In the last book ...

- Max and Tiger looked for the CODE key on the green planet.
- The BITE and his jets attacked!
- Max and Tiger fell down a pit. How will they escape?

**CODE key
(1 collected)**

You are in the
Galactic Orbit zone.

Before you read

Sound checker
Say the sounds.

ar   or
ur   er

Sound spotter
Blend the sounds.

| f | or |

| s | t | ar |

| b | ur | s | t | s |

| b | oo | s | t | er |

Tricky word

she

Into the zone

Who do you think will
rescue Max and Tiger?

4

Jet Pack Cat

Is that a shooting star in the dark night?
No! It is a jet.

Jet Facts

The jet belongs to the BITE.

thin wings
(for turning fast)

sharp parts

Mini checks jet facts on her Gizmo.

Jet Facts

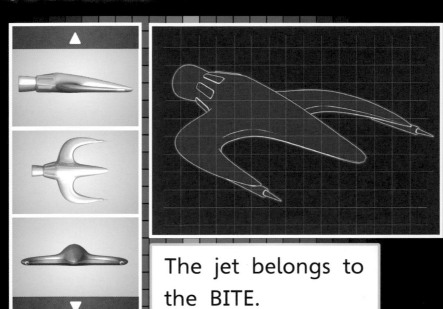

The jet belongs to the BITE.

sharp parts

thin wings
(for turning fast)

The BITE has a jet but Cat has her jet pack.
She can go fast!

Cat can press the speed booster
for quick bursts to go faster.

Can Cat go faster than the jet?
Or will the jet go faster
than Cat?

I will look for
Max and Tiger.

Now you have read ...
Jet Pack Cat

Text checker

Look back at the story.
Find a fact about the jet.

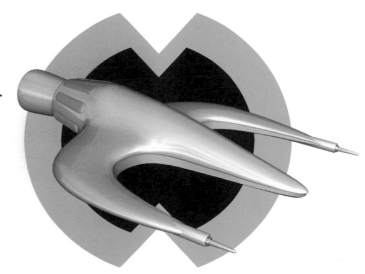

MITE fun

What can Cat do with her
jet pack? How might she
rescue Max and Tiger?
Help her to make a plan.

I can go fast!

Before you read

Sound checker
Say the sounds.

ar   or
ur   er

Sound spotter
Blend the sounds.

c	or	d

t	ur	n

sh	ar	p

t	r	a	ck	er

Tricky words
are
she
he
me
they

Into the zone
How might Cat find
Max and Tiger?

12

Cat is a Star!

Max and Tiger are stuck in the pit. Tiger turns on his torch but it is still too dark.

Cat looks at her watch.
She sees Max on her tracker.

Cat gets her torch.
She turns it on.
She looks into the pit.

Max and Tiger can see Cat now. Max shoots out his cord.

Cat!

Tiger holds on to the cord but his arm hits a sharp rock!

He is not hurt.
Max and Tiger go up.

It is the jets.
The BITE is back!

Max and Tiger run but the jets are too quick.

The jets turn to get Cat but she can go faster.

Cat shrinks.
The jets can not see her.

Max and Tiger run.

Team X and Mini are safe but not for long.
They will see the BITE again soon.

Now you have read ...
Cat is a Star!

Text checker

What kit did Cat use in this story?
How did she use it?
Read each label and find the
kit in the picture.

jet pack

watch   torch

MITE fun

Look at the pictures.
What makes Cat a star?